Gavin and Errol and Sophie

and Sushma and David and Kate

and Robert and Alison are . . .

...Starting
School

Janet and Allan Ahlberg

PUFFIN

For
Val Dwelly, who gave us the idea
and
Birstall Riverside Primary School, who let us in.

The First Day

The children wait
in the playground

with their mums and
dads and brothers and
sisters ... and a puppy.

The bell rings.

Gavin and Errol

and Sophie and

Sushma and David

and Kate and Robert and Alison

go into the school

and meet their teacher.

They hang

their hats and

coats in the cloakroom, have a look

at the toilets and go

into the classroom. They sit on the mat

with the rest of the class.

The teacher calls the register and collects the dinner money.

She shows the children round the classroom, and the parents too.

In the classroom there are tables chairs and drawers for the children to keep their things in. There is ...

Gavin Taylor

they go out to play.

At dinner time they eat their dinners.

In the afternoon they draw pictures,

go out to play again and have

singing in the hall.

At the end of the day they

tidy up,

have a story on the mat,

put on their hats and coats –

and go home.

The Second Day

The next day Gavin and Errol and

Sophie and Sushma and David and

Kate and Robert and Alison

go to school again.

In the morning they do a picture

and some writing in their new books.

 After that they

have music and

movement in the hall.

 Errol's mum plays the piano.

At play time Robert loses his hat...and Alison finds it.

Errol bangs his knee,

and the teacher rubs it better.

Gavin and Sushma and David climb on the climbing frame.

Kate <u>thinks</u> about climbing.

In the afternoon the children make

some models.

They show them to the

head teacher, have a story

on the mat and go home.

The First Week

As the days go by,

the children

get more used to the school.

On Wednesday they go into the hall
for assembly.

They listen to the
singing and say
a prayer.

They watch some older children do
a play.

On Thursday they
start learning to read.

Run, run as fast
as you can.

"Stop, stop little boy"
Said the horse

He jumped onto
the fox's back.

Gavin can read already.

He brings his book from home
to show the teacher.

Errol brings his <u>tooth</u>
to show the teacher.

It came out in the night.

On Friday they go swimming in the school pool.

The water is warm and not deep. Robert and Sushma and Kate jump up and down.

David and Sophie walk in down the steps. Errol thinks about walking in.

In the afternoon Kate and Sushma and David do cooking with David's mum.

They make 12 little cakes,

3 big cakes

...and a mess.

Time Goes By

The next week Gavin and

Errol and Sophie

and Sushma

and David

and Kate

and

Robert and Alison . . .

choose a name for the rabbit.

 They draw rabbit pictures,

make rabbit models,

bake rabbit biscuits,

have rabbit stories on the mat, and do

lots more rabbit

things besides.

The week after that the children
have their photographs taken.

Sometimes
the teacher is not
cheerful either.

End of Term

Christmas comes.

In the last week of term the infants

do a play about

baby Jesus.

Everybody has a part,

and all the mums

and dads come

to watch.

On the last <u>day</u> of term

the children bring cakes

and crisps,

sausages, sandwiches

and jellies, and have a party

in the classroom.

Merry Christmas Ronald

Then Gavin and Errol
and Sophie

and Sushma

and Kate

and David

and Robert and Alison
go home...

and the holiday begins.